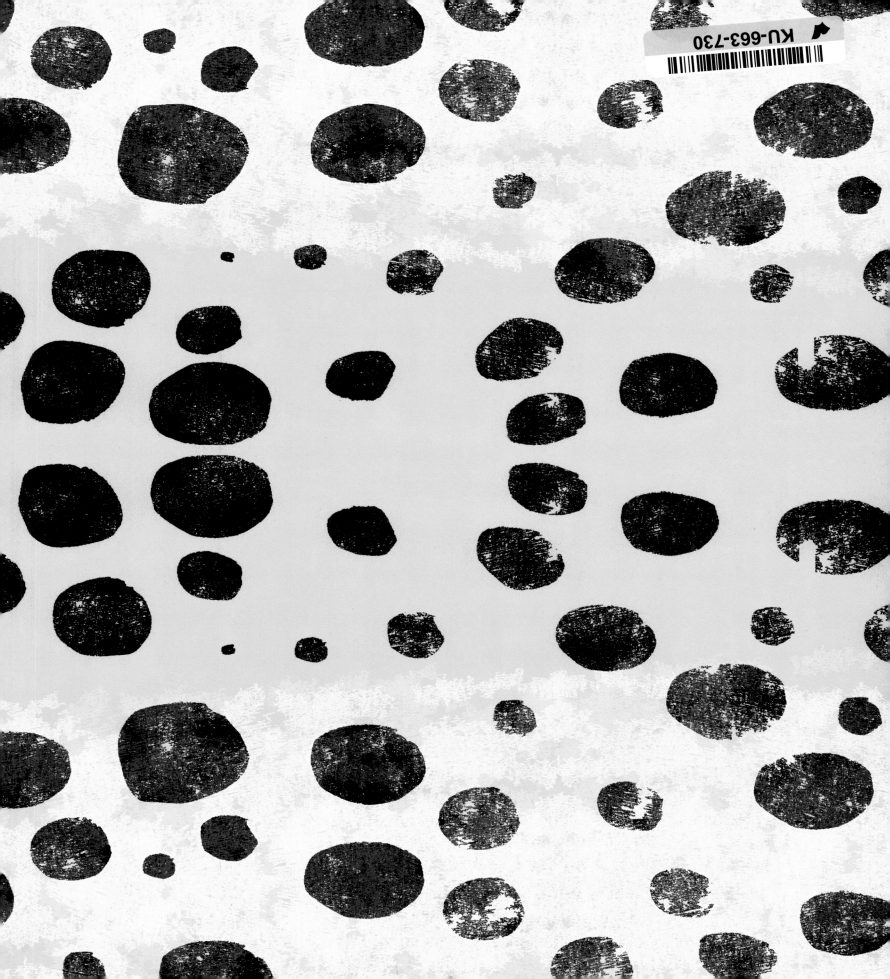

ORCHARD BOOKS

338 Euston Road, London NW1 3BH

Orchard Books Australia

Level 17/207 Kent Street, Sydney, NSW 2000

First published in 2011 by Orchard Books

First published in paperback in 2012

ISBN 978 1 40830 472 3

Text and illustrations © Emma Dodd 2011

The right of Emma Dodd to be identified as the author and illustrator of
this work has been asserted by her in accordance with the Copyright,
Designs and Patents Act, 1988.

A CIP catalogue record for this book is available from the British Library.

10 9 8 7 6 5 4 3 2 1

Printed in China

Orchard Books is a division of Hachette Children's Books,
an Hachette UK company.

www.hachette.co.uk

For Fay Dodd
with all my love
Emma xx

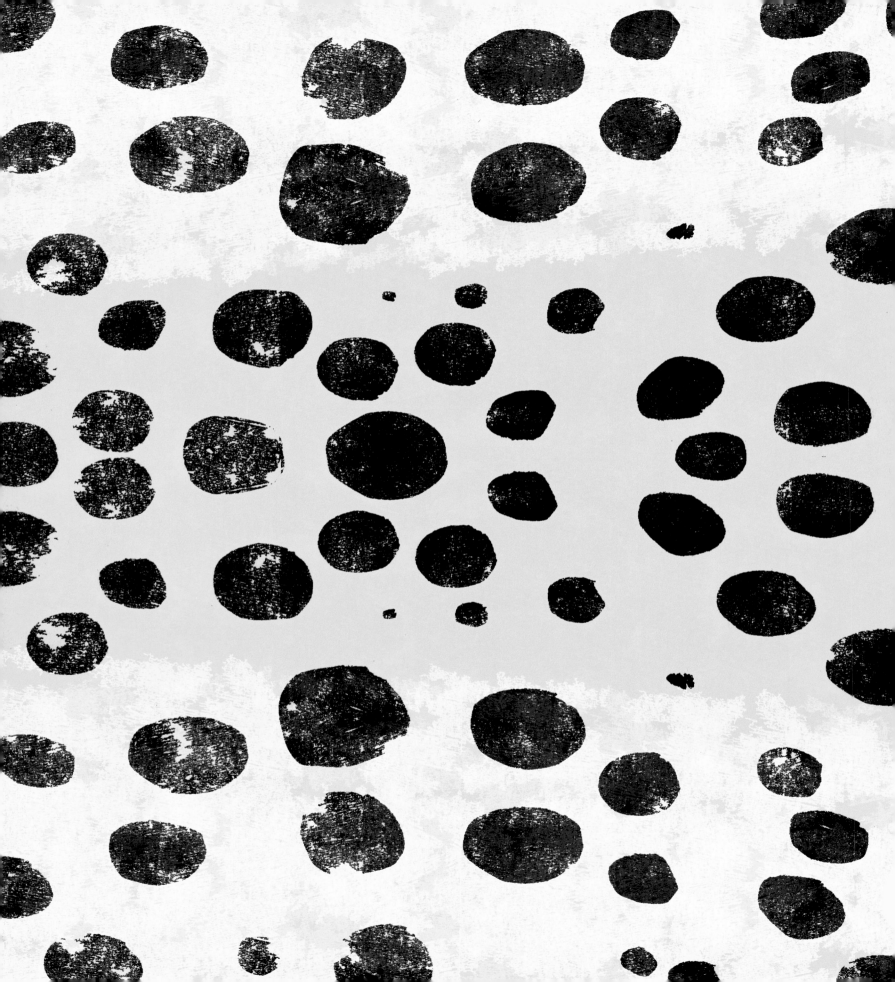

I Love Beasts!

Emma Dodd

ORCHARD

I Love Bugs!

I love all beasts,

great and small beasts.

I love whales in the deep blue ocean

and **reptiles**
in low,
slow-motion.

The gorilla who beats his chest and the ant-eater eating up pests.

I love cheetahs who are super-fast and the snail who always comes last.

I'm keen on skunks, as well, even though they really do smell!!

Yes I really do
I love the
kangaroo

and the grumpy, humpy camel too.

I love

elephants, saggy and trunky

and even this
funny-faced
monkey!

Extinct dinosaurs
rather appeal

Though I'm glad
I won't meet one
for **real!**

Yes, I really do adore beasts,

all the land and shore beasts.

But the very best
of all beasts
is not
beastly
in the
least

A well-loved brown bear.
A cosy, snuggle down
bear.

A cuddle-me-tight bear,
A bear who'll always
be there.

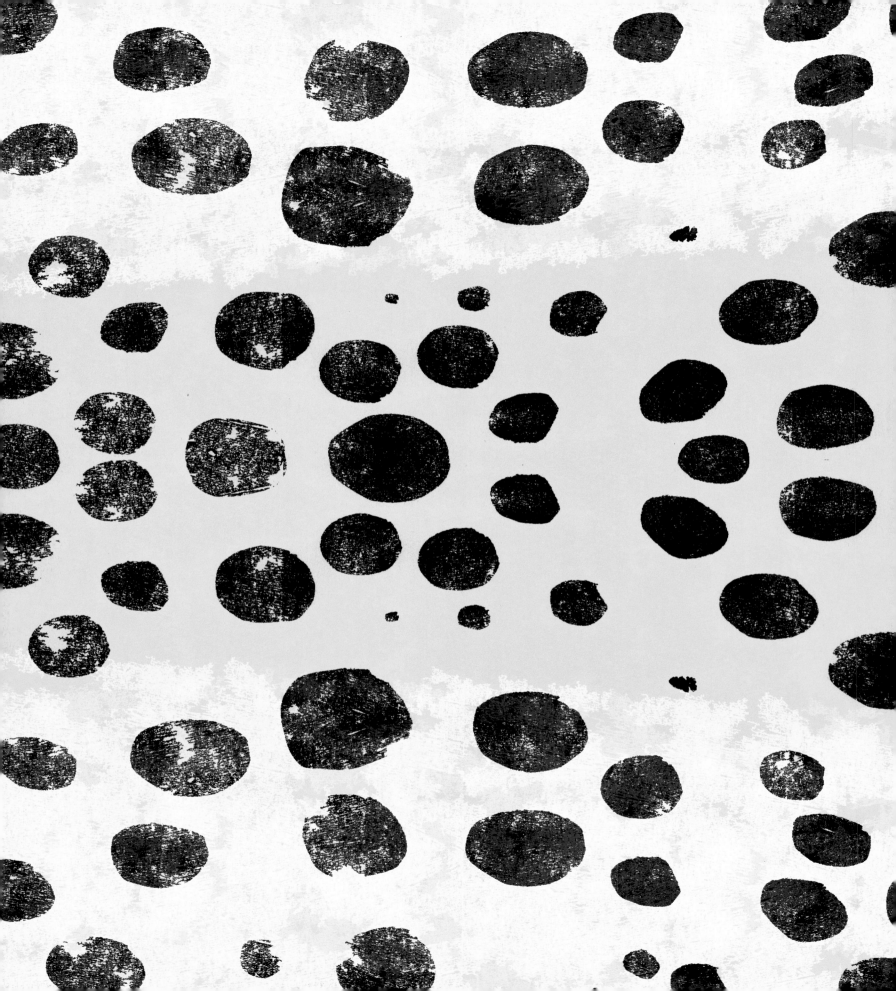

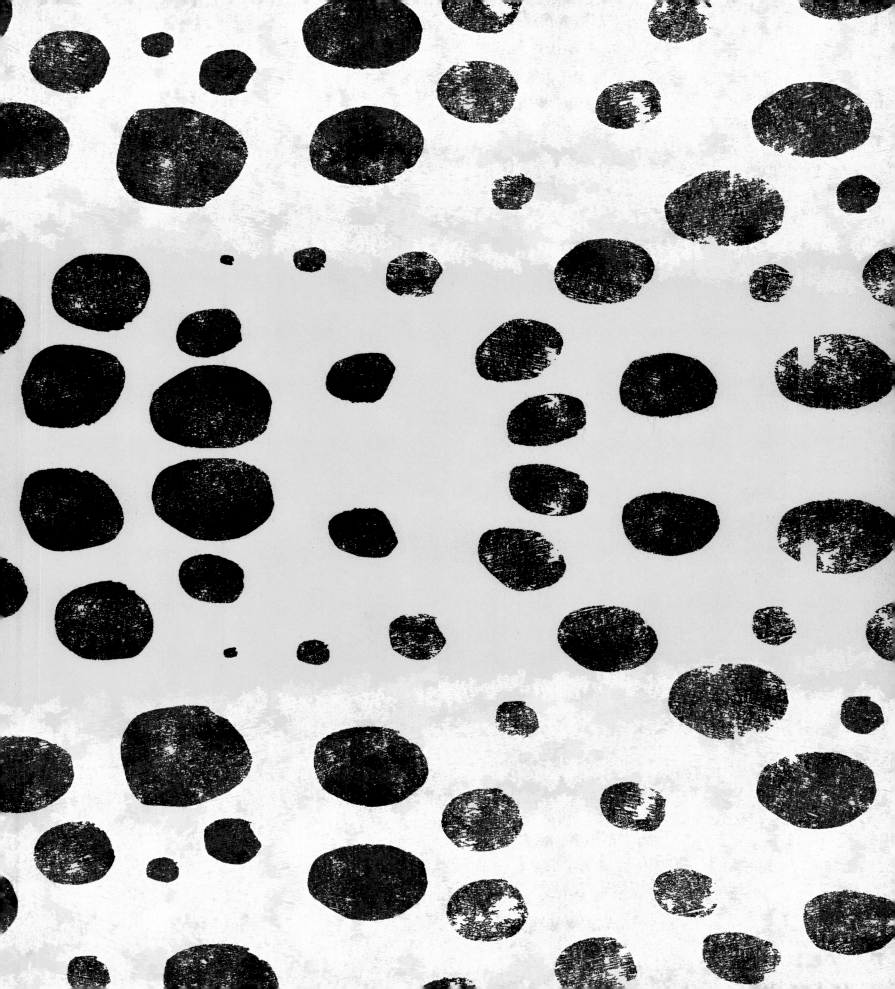

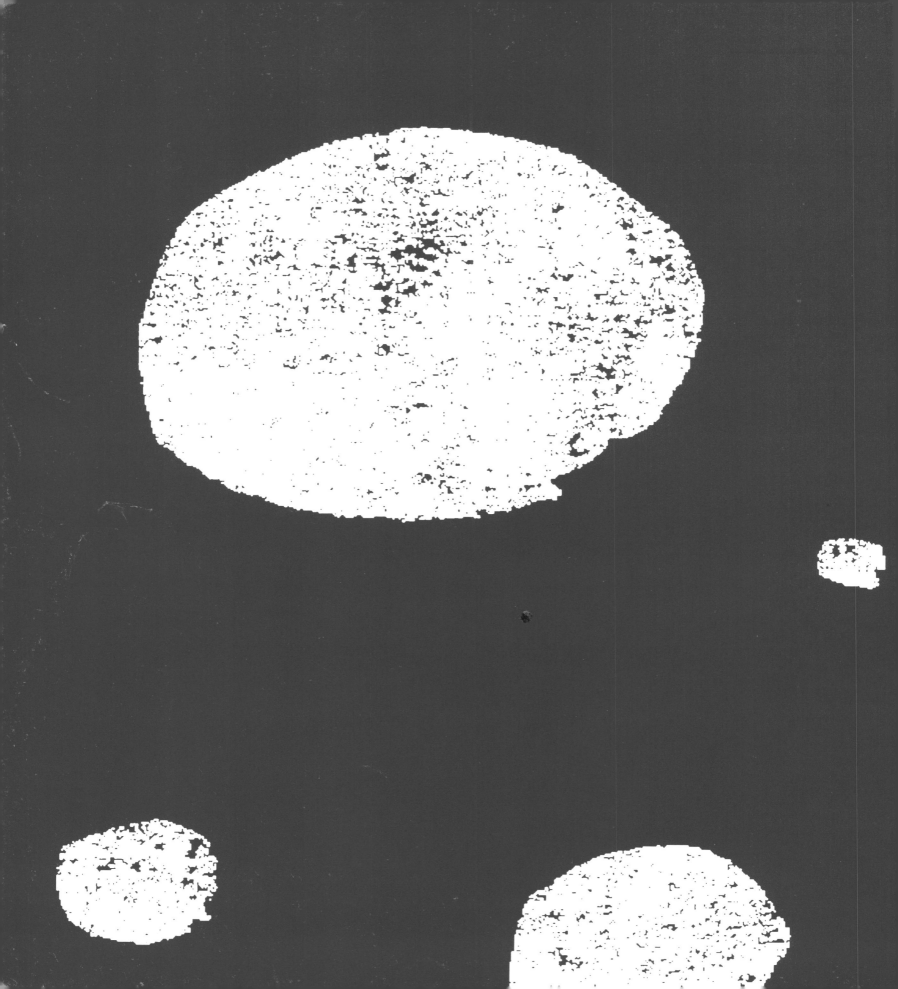